Contents

My shark dream
Digraph review 3

A fresh feast
Digraph review 12

Bears at the fair
Focus on: air, ear as in *f<u>air</u>, p<u>ear</u>* 23

A fairy story
Focus on: air, ear as in *f<u>air</u>, y<u>ear</u>* 27

Phonemes: ch, sh, th, wh, ph, a_e, ai, ay, e_e, ea, ee, y *as e*, i_e, ie, igh, y *as i,* o_e, oa, ow, u_e, ue, oo, ew, ar, or, er, ir, ur, wr, oo, u, oy, oi, aw, au, ow, ou, <mark>air, ear</mark> **'Tricky' words:** my, can't, does, love, here, are, look, our, eyes, house, were, little, <mark>all</mark>, <mark>friend</mark>

About this book

These short stories are designed to give children blending and reading practice. They are decodable, which means the words in them only include letter shapes and sounds that the children have learned. The stories gradually introduce 'tricky' words, building on the learning in the Red Series.

The progression links directly to the teaching order in the Letterland teaching range. Each story begins with a title page that provides important information for children and teachers.

Story title

Focus on: New spelling patterns introduced

New 'tricky' words: Common words with irregular spellings

Basic teaching tips:

- Encourage the sounding out of decodable words (and any decodable parts of 'tricky' words).
- Discuss the stories with the children to ensure comprehension and engagement.
- Encourage re-reading in pairs or individually to develop fluency and reading for meaning.

Red Series introduces the a-z letters and sounds and some 'tricky words'. On completion of this series, the following words remain tricky in part: **a, the, she, oh, for, that, ok, they, says, her, this, to, said, of, what, you, was, want, come, sees, asks, do.** These words are included in **Blue Series**.

My shark dream

Digraph review

On Saturday, Dad took me and Pip on a trip.
We went to see the sharks in big tanks.

"Do you like sharks?" asked Pip.

"I like them a lot," I said.

"I had a dream last night. A shark had hurt its fin and had been washed up on to the beach."

"What did you do?" asked Pip.

"In my dream I pulled it back to the sea!"

"Then, in my dream, the shark swam off and it was fine. I felt happy, but then it swam back to me and opened its huge mouth!"

"Oh no! Then what happened?" asked Pip.

"The shark's teeth looked sharp. I tried to scream but I just woke up instead! It was just a silly dream."

"I'm glad the sharks we will see today are in tanks," said Pip.

When we got to the tanks there were lots of different sharks. We enjoyed looking at them. It was interesting reading about them, too.

"That's a Short Fin Mako," I said.
"It can swim really fast."

Pip liked that shark. He said he can swim fast like that, too!

"This person is swimming with the sharks!"

"Wow! She is brave," said Pip.

"It says here she likes to study sharks. She says a lot of sharks are harmless."

"I hope I will dream about a harmless shark tonight!" said Pip.

"Me too! I think I like sharks a lot more now I have seen them in the tanks," I said.

A fresh feast

Digraph review

On a sunny day in Spring, Golden Girl and her Gran were sitting in the garden.

Golden Girl was reading the book, 'The Red Hen.'

She began reading this part…

"The cat, the dog and the pig did not help the Red Hen. That is mean!" Golden Girl said to her Gran.

"And look! At the end of the book, the cat, the dog, and the pig want to eat the food. But they did not help to grow it! I hope my pals don't do that!" said Golden Girl.

The next day her pals came to the garden.

"Will you help me grow a few plants in my garden? First we will have to do a lot of digging," she said.

Peter Puppy said, "Yes! I will help."
His paws were perfect for digging so he dug, and dug, and dug for her.

Then Ben came along in his blue boots.

Ben said, "Yes! I will help."

"I have a packet of black beans for you. They will grow well in your garden. Let me plant them."

Munching Mike said, "Yes! I will help."

Mike loves munching on melons so he planted melons for Golden Girl.

The plants grew and grew. When it was time to pick the crops, Golden Girl and her Gran filled a basket. There was a lot of fresh food!

Vicky came to help out, too.

"My pals are kind," said Golden Girl.
"They helped me grow the food in my garden.
Now I am happy to eat it with them!"

Her pals arrived for lunch. It was a fresh feast.

"Thank you for helping me in my garden," said Golden Girl.

"Thank you for this yummy fresh feast!" they said.

Bears at the fair

Tricky word: all

Focus on: air, ear as in _fair_, _pear_

It was the first morning of the funfair. There were all sorts of contests and stalls.

"I'd like to get an eclair," said Eddy Elephant.

"I'd like that perfect pear tart," said Peter Puppy.

"Well, I'm going to do the dressing up show," said Dippy Duck.

"I don't know what to do," said Bouncy Ben, in despair.

"I want to dress up, I want to see the knights fighting, I want to see a puppet show and I also want to go in a hot air balloon, but I can't do it all."

Just then, Ben's brother had a brainwave.

Ben and his brother dressed up as bears and went up in the hot air balloon!

From up in the balloon they could see *everything* at the fair below.

"Look up there! A pair of bears in the air! That's the best show at the fair!" all the Letterlanders agreed.

A fairy story

Tricky word: friend

Focus on: air, ear as in *fair*, *year*

My friend, Claire, likes to tell me a story about a fairy. She says it comes to visit her room at night.

Claire says the fairy comes nearly every night. It appears when it thinks she is asleep. If she gets up, it disappears into thin air.

Claire says the fairy just pops up by her ear.
She can hear the little wings beating near to her.

The fairy has no fear. Claire can even feel it breathing in her ear!

Claire says every year there's a party and her fairy brings lots of friends. The girls have fair hair and clear wings. The boys have beards and tiny red boots. They all jump on her bed and giggle.

I don't think Claire's fairy story is true, but it is still lots of fun to hear it!

About this series

This series of 10 books accompanies the Letterland teaching range. Each book contains a selection of short stories. In total there are 32 engaging stories featuring the phonic elements listed below as well as some 'tricky' high-frequency words.

Book	Focus elements	As in the word...	Story titles
1	sh, ch, th, th, wh, ph	chip, shop, that, thing	Check on the chicks / Shep and me / What is that thing?
2	a_e, ai, ay	make, rain, say,	A safe place / Kate bakes a cake / Kane's tail!
3	e_e, ea, ee, y	these, sea, bee, baby	A trip to the sea / Mr E's trees / Happy!
4	i_e, ie, igh, y	like, tie, night, my	Ben rides his bike / Cats at night / What a mess!
5	o_e, oa, ow	home, boat, show	The bad goat / When the cold wind blows / Lost in the Queen's maze
6	u_e, ue, oo, ew	cube, blue, moon, few, grew	Stuck on a dune / A day at the zoo / The Hat Man's new roof
7	ar, or, er, ir, ur, wr	farm, for, her, girl, fur, write	The big match / Snapshots / The bird girls / My very bad morning
8	o, oo, u, oy, oi	son, book, put, boy, coin	Oscar's brother / The big pull / Nick's noisy new toy
9	aw, au, ow, ou	saw, cause, how, out,	Draw it! / The house mouse / Look now!
10	Review ear, air	pear, year, fair	My shark dream / A fresh feast / Bears at the fair / A fairy story

Collect the sets

Phonics Readers - Red Series

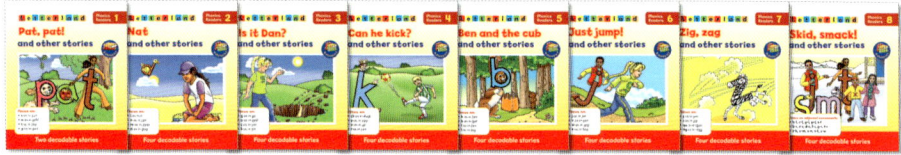

Phonics Readers - Blue Series

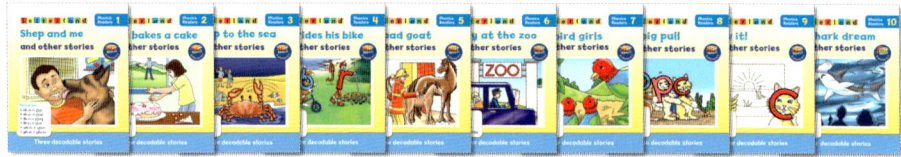

Published by Letterland International Ltd. 8/10 South Street, Epsom, Surrey, KT18 7PF, UK.
www.letterland.com
ISBN: 978-1-78248-189-8
Product Code: TJ11

© Letterland International 2016
LETTERLAND™ is a trademark of Letterland International Ltd.

First published 2013. This new edition published 2016.
Reprinted 2023.
10 9 8 7 6 5 4 3 2

Authors: Stamey Carter and Lisa Holt
Originator of Letterland: Lyn Wendon
Artwork: Doreen Shaw
Design: Lisa Holt

The author asserts the moral right to be identified as the author of this work. All rights reserved. No part of this publication may be reproduced, stored in a retrieval system, or transmitted in any form or by any means, electronic, mechanical, photocopying, recording or otherwise, without either the prior permission of the Publisher or a licence permitting restricted copying in the United Kingdom issued by the Copyright Licensing Agency Ltd, 90 Tottenham Court Road, London W1T 4LP. This book is sold subject to the condition that it shall not be by way of trade or otherwise be lent, hired out or otherwise circulated without the Publisher's prior consent.

Printed in Beirut, Lebanon.